The Fisherman and His Wife

Contents

The Fisherman and His Wife
A traditional tale   2

The Fisherman's Warning
A poem   21

Staying Alive
A mind map and fish facts   22

Housing Hubbub at Halibut Bay
A newspaper report   24

Make a Wish Fish
Instructions   26

Palace for a Day
A play   28

Think and Link
Questions to discuss   32

A fisherman lived in a hut by the sea, but that wasn't where his wife wanted to be.

Each day as she mended
the nets stitch by stitch,
she sighed and she cried,
"How I'd love to be rich!"
She sighed and she cried,
"How I'd love to be rich!"

One day something happened
to make their lives change.
The fisherman found something
terribly strange.

A fish that could talk
came up out of the sea.
He knew it was magic,
so he set it free.
He knew it was magic,
so he set it free.

His wife was annoyed
when she heard of that fish.
"If it's magic," she said,
"it can grant me a wish."

"You must go and find it –
now do not delay.
I want a new house,
and I want it today!"
*She wanted a house
on the very same day!*

The fisherman set off
at his wife's request.
He knew if he didn't
she'd give him no rest.

He called to the fish
where it swam in the sea –
and it granted the wish,
for he'd set it free.
It granted the wish,
for he'd set it free.

His wife was contented
for just a short while.
Then she said that a mansion
was much more her style.

"This place is too small.
I need rooms long and wide.
If I had a mansion,
I'd be satisfied."
With a mansion, she said,
she would be satisfied.

The fisherman set out
and found the strange fish.
Dark clouds filled the sky
as it granted the wish.

He returned to a mansion
and riches galore –
but in no time at all
his wife wanted much more!
*In no time at all
his wife wanted much more.*

"I want a palace,"
she said with a sneer.
"I'll sit on a throne
while the people all cheer."

So again the poor fisherman
went to the fish.
It looked very angry
but granted the wish.

*It looked very angry
but granted the wish.*

But in a grand palace,
with jewels and a throne,
his wife still complained.
Yes, still she did moan.

"I want more importance.
I know what I'm worth,
and I wish to be Emperor
of the whole Earth!"
*She wished to be Emperor
of the whole Earth!*

"Oh, no!" cried the fisherman,
trembling with fear.
"I cannot ask that.
Please don't make me, my dear."

But alas! She insisted
he find the strange fish.
A storm raged and roared
as he whispered the wish.
*A storm raged and roared
as he whispered the wish.*

"Oh, no!" the fish thundered.
"This is far too much greed!
But I'll give your wife something –
a big change indeed."

The fisherman saw
what he meant back on shore.
All they had was the hut
that they'd lived in before!
All they had was the hut
that they'd lived in before!
And they never saw
that magic fish any more.

The Fisherman's Warning

Fishing, fishing, fishing,
Watch what's in your net.
If fishing turns to wishing,
Beware of what you get.

Fishing, fishing, fishing,
You mustn't look for magic.
If fishing turns to wishing,
The outcome could be tragic.

Fishing, fishing, fishing,
You shouldn't ask for more.
If fishing turns to wishing,
Then you might end up poor.

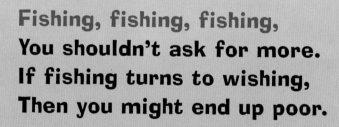

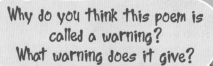

Why do you think this poem is
called a warning?
What warning does it give?

21

Most fish have no magic to keep them alive,
so what do they do to help them survive?
These pages will give you some facts to explore.
Use them as a start. Research and write more.

Staying Alive

being very poisonous

Fish protect themselves by

having bony scales or plates

hiding

swimming fast

living with bigger fish

having spines

living in big groups called schools

Striped catfish live in schools to keep safe.

Sargassum fish look like the seaweed in which they live.

Lion fish have poison in their spines.

Yellowfin tuna swim fast to escape their predators.

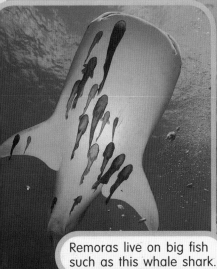

Remoras live on big fish such as this whale shark.

Sea horses have bony plates to protect them.

Porcupine fish are covered in spines. When they are frightened, they puff themselves up with water.

Housing Hubbub
at Halibut Bay

Palace appeared overnight, say locals.

Something strange is happening at Halibut Bay, home of fisherman Henry Hook and his wife, Helga.

Mr. Luke Seaward told the *Seaside Times* that there have been four different buildings at Halibut Bay in four days. "The Hooks have always had a hut by the sea," he said. "But on Friday it was a house. On Saturday it was a mansion. On Sunday

Henry and Helga Hook

it was a palace. Ther on Monday it was a hut again. People shouldn't be allowed to change houses whenever they like. And that palace was blocking my view!"

Mrs. Mimi Furst, of Sardines Crossing, told us that she had been invited to the Hooks' palace. "Most of the village was there. That Helga sat on a throne and wanted us to cheer her!"

Mr. Blindus A. Bat, of Halibut Hill, says Mr. Seaward and Mrs. Furst are mistaken. "Look out of that window," he told us. "It's a hut. It always has been. They must be seeing things."

The *Seaside Times* will continue to fish for answers.

Halibut Hut

Make a Wish fish

Stained glass fish

You will need:

 Cellophane

 Glue   White pencil

 Black paper

Scissors

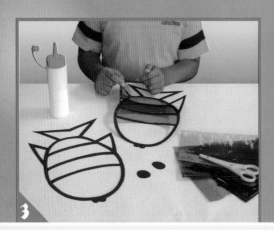

1 Draw two matching fish on black paper. Cut them out.

2 Cut matching shapes out of both fish. You can ask an adult to help.

3 Glue cellophane over the shapes in one fish.

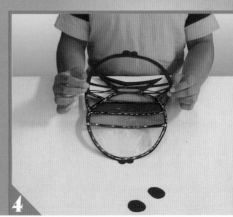

4 Stick the two fish together, with the cellophane between them.

6

Glue an eye on your fish.

Hang your fish in the light.

What other ways of making fish could you try?

Write instructions for a friend.

Palace for a Day

A Play

Cast

Magic Fish
Henry Hook
Helga Hook
Mimi Furst
Luke Seaward
Other Guests

SCENE 1 *At sea, early morning.*

Magic Fish: So now you want a palace?

Henry Hook: Er, yes, sir. My wife says that a palace will definitely make her happy.

Magic Fish: Very well, I'll grant you this wish. But it must be the last one.

SCENE 2 *The palace, later that morning.*

Helga Hook: This is perfect! I'm sure I was born to live in a palace. Why else would you have found that magic fish?

Henry Hook: Yes, my dear. Now, let's have breakfast.

Helga Hook: *(Ignoring him)* But there is something missing. What could it be?

Henry Hook: Breakfast?

Helga Hook: *(Ignoring him)* I know! People! What's the point of having a palace if people can't see you in it?

Henry Hook: My dear, everyone will be having their breakfast. Why don't *we* have some, too?

Helga Hook: *(Ignoring him)* Go around the village, Henry. Tell all the people they are invited to our new palace at noon. The poor things will be dying to see it.

Henry Hook: But, my dear, I...

Helga Hook: Run along now, Henry. I'll sit here on my throne. Just wait till Mimi Furst sees me in my crown!

SCENE 3 *The palace, noon. The guests arrive.*

Helga Hook: How lovely to see you. Do sit down. I'll be over here, on my *THRONE.*

Mimi Furst: Harrumph.

Helga Hook: Did you say something, Mimi? If you want to cheer, please do. It *is* rather exciting, isn't it?

Mimi Furst: *HAARRUUUUMPH!*

Helga Hook: Mimi, my dear, are you feeling all right?

Mimi Furst: I was all right until I came here. What do you need a palace for? It's ridiculous.

Luke Seaward: You can't just put a palace wherever you like. You're blocking my view!

Helga Hook: *(Rising from her throne)* Well, really! You're just jealous. Henry, tell them to show me some respect.

Mimi Furst: Respect! You have to *earn* respect. Come on, everyone. We're leaving!

The guests leave the palace.

Helga Hook: *(Shouting after them)* I wanted you to go, anyway! *(She bursts into tears.)*

Henry Hook: Never mind, my dear. We'll both feel better after a good lunch.

Helga Hook: How can you think about lunch? Didn't you see how they treated me? Well, I'll show them. You'll have to tell that fish to make me Emperor of the Earth! *Now!*

Henry Hook: *(Trembling)* Oh no, my dear! Please don't make me ask that! Why don't you eat something? A little lunch...

Helga Hook: Find that fish! *GO!*

SCENE 4 *At sea, that evening.*

Magic Fish: *(Angrily)* Emperor of the Earth! Don't worry, I'll give your wife a change! A *big* change!

Henry Hook: Er, thank you, sir. You're very kind. And, umm, I wonder if you could manage to bring me something to eat while you're at it?

THE END

Think and Link

Rhyme and Repetition

Where do you find rhyme and repetition in the story and in the poem? What do rhyme and repetition add to these texts?

Newspaper Report and Play

Which characters are in both the newspaper report and the play, but not in the story? Do you find out more about these characters from the newspaper report or from the play? Why?

Staying Alive and the Wish Fish

Why do you think these sections of the book both use photographs instead of illustrations? Do they use photos in the same ways or in different ways? How?

Fact and Fantasy

Which parts of the book relate to things that happen in the real world? How? Which parts of the book would you call fantasy? Why?

Fish Pictures

Which of the drawings and photographs of fish in this book do you like most? Why?